P9-DHT-760

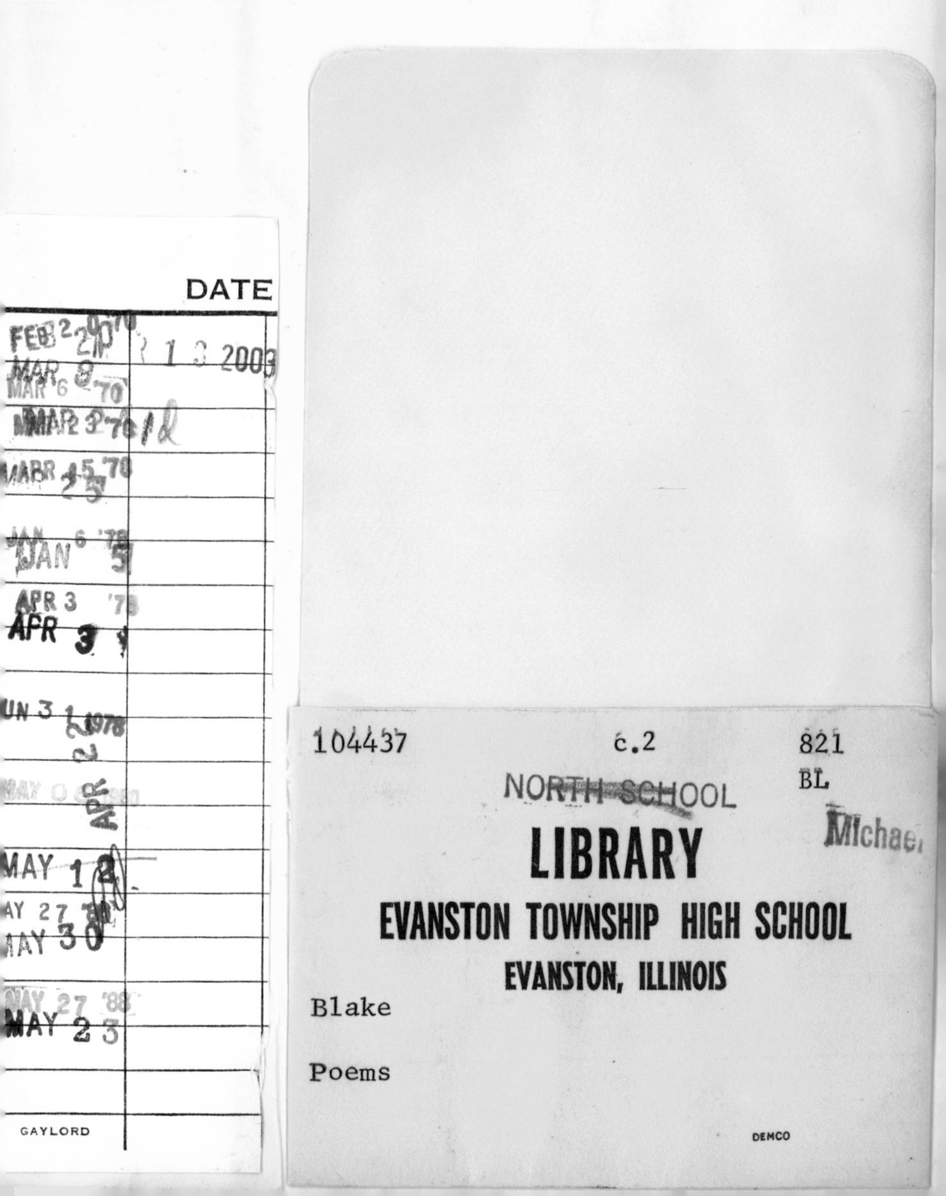
DATE
GAYLORD
104437
c.2
821
BL
NORTH SCHOOL
LIBRARY
EVANSTON TOWNSHIP HIGH SCHOOL
EVANSTON, ILLINOIS
Blake
Poems
DEMCO

Poems of WILLIAM BLAKE

LAMBETH
Printed by Will: Blake 1794

Poems of William BLAKE

SELECTED BY AMELIA H. MUNSON

ILLUSTRATIONS BY WILLIAM BLAKE

THOMAS Y. CROWELL COMPANY NEW YORK

Designed by Albert Burkhardt

Manufactured in the United States of America

Library of Congress Catalog Card No. 64-22542

2 3 4 5 6 7 8 9 10

Grateful acknowledgment is made
to the Pierpont Morgan Library for permission
to use the four woodcuts from the PASTORALS
of Vergil and the frontispiece from EUROPA.

CONTENTS

WILLIAM BLAKE, ONE WHO IS VERY MUCH DELIGHTED WITH BEING IN GOOD COMPANY. BORN 28 NOVR 1757 IN LONDON & HAS DIED SEVERAL TIMES SINCE.

Inscription in the Autograph Album of William Upcott
January 16, 1826

This characteristically worded inscription was written a year or so before Blake's death, and if he felt then that he had already "died several times," it was not without reason. At the present time, however, William Blake is very much alive. His songs are set to music, his writings have become a treasure trove for scholars and researchers, and a so-called Age of Revolutions welcomes him as a great, rebellious forerunner.

He was born in the middle of the eighteenth century (in 1757) and lived through the first quarter of the nineteenth (until 1827), but not until the twentieth century has there been a full understanding and appreciation of his genius. Of course he was recognized earlier both as a poet and as an artist; he was even acclaimed by the knowing in his own day, and a group of young "disciples" clustered about him in his last years. But much of his fervor was mistaken for madness and his independent, creative thought for fanatical eccentricity. His generation could have accepted him as an Old Testament prophet with his visions and exhortations, but not for what he actually was—a citizen of a new age.

Blake was only eighteen when, in his words,

> a mighty and awful change threatened the Earth. The American War began. All its dark horrors passed before my face.

His whole being responded to the cry for liberty, and, like many other Englishmen of his day, he cried out against his government's intransigence. He befriended Tom Paine when London became for him a danger spot. His long poem, "America, A Prophecy," conveys his high hopes for the new world that America should become, and not only America, but England as well. The loss of America, however, did not change the Empire. Then came the French Revolution, and again Blake was swept up by the fervor for liberty. But, as the totality of that revolution unrolled, disillusionment followed, together with a deep despondency over the role his country chose to play then and in the aftermath.

> The stern Bard ceas'd, asham'd of his own song:
> enrag'd he swung
> His harp aloft sounding, then dash'd its shining
> frame against
> A ruin'd pillar in glitt'ring fragments: silent he
> turn'd away,
> And wander'd down the vales of Kent in sick &
> drear lamentings.

Blake's own life was endangered because of his republican sentiments. Just as Milton, foreign secretary in Cromwell's government, had to go into hiding after the fall of that government and the coming of the Restoration, so the humble Blake, who had never even moved in government circles, had to find ways of disguising his intense disapproval of the reign of George III. This he did by such skillful use of symbolic language and irony in his poetry that readers are frequently confused. He realized that physical conflict was not to be the answer, that victory must be sought on a higher plane, and he dedicated himself to its attainment,

> I will not cease from Mental Fight,
> Nor shall my Sword sleep in my hand
> Till we have built Jerusalem
> In England's green & pleasant Land.

And again,

> I care not whether a man is Good or Evil; all that I
> care
> Is whether he is a Wise Man or a Fool. Go! put off
> Holiness,
> And put on Intellect. . . .

So absorbing a character is Blake that one is tempted to continue drawing out one strand of his life and interlacing it with his own words, and to neglect the many other threads that make up the tapestry. To call him a rebel is not to describe the whole man. He has also been called a mystic and a visionary. As a boy of eight, he saw on Peckham Rye a tree filled with angels; later he saw angels in a field nearby. His wise father, a Swedenborgian, recognized the differences inherent in his son and valued them; he also foresaw the difficulties that might beset him. The boy was therefore kept from school, but never from learning, and all his life Blake reveled in self-education. At ten, he showed such delight and promise in drawing that he was allowed to take drawing lessons. At fourteen, he was apprenticed to an engraver, and, after being grounded in his craft, was turned loose in Westminster Abbey to sketch the tombs, marble figures, and tablets that peopled the place with England's history and literature. The miracle of Gothic architecture enveloped him, and its glory never left him. For five enraptured years he lived in this atmosphere.

From his twelfth to his twentieth year, he was also writing down the poems that took form in his mind. These were collected by a well-meaning older friend and printed, without Blake's knowledge, as *Poetical Sketches*. Fortunately, they have been preserved—though Blake himself did not seem to care for them as he grew older—and selections from the *Sketches* form the first section of this book.

The very first poem, "To the Muses," in spite of its eighteenth-century manner, might very well have been written in our own day, or perhaps in any other, since poets are always being assailed for not being sufficiently poetic. Blake disguises his attack on the poets by charging the Muses themselves with forsaking poetry:

How have you left the antient lore
  That bards of old enjoy'd in you!
The languid strings do scarcely move!
  The sound is forc'd, the notes are few!

Many of his verses have become widely known and so often quoted that they are part of our common usage. Best known are his "Songs of Innocence," whose depth of meaning has often been overlooked, so simple and innocent is their sound. But the man who wrote "Innocence dwells with Wisdom but never with Ignorance" did not expect his verses to be read unthinkingly. Blake is a wonderfully rewarding poet. New discoveries are still to be made, not only in the meaning, but in discoveries of the poems themselves, for not all that Blake is supposed to have written has yet come to light.

The necessity of hiding his real thoughts extended to his religious poems, for dissension here was also dangerous. In his effort to be outspoken and cryptic simultaneously, Blake created a whole mythology, with new names and symbols. This divergence from orthodoxy caused much confusion even among his admirers, and still does, as when he says, "Thy Heaven doors are my Hell gates." But he was unworried. He declares,

I am in God's presence night and day
And he never turns his face away.

For the most part, he went his confident way even when it was solitary and when his years of neglect would have daunted a lesser man. He could always depend upon the utter faith and devotion of his wife, even though there might be nothing in the house to eat and no prospects ahead. "I have very little of Mr. Blake's company," she once confided to a visitor, "he is always in Paradise." But Blake himself had plenty of company; he was surrounded by the creatures of his own fancy and his lively and remarkable visual imagination. "I can look at a knot in a piece of wood," he tells us, "until I am frightened by it."

To the end, Blake had his visions, which were more real to him than reality. Great men of all times and all countries appeared to him, usually at night, and kept his pencil busy as he sketched them. They also dictated to him, he believed, long sections of his poems, though he did not hesitate to make changes in some of the passages later.

He always maintained that it was in a vision his favorite brother, Robert, appeared to him a year after his death, when William was about thirty years old, and revealed the secret of what he called "illuminated printing." This was a method Blake had been searching for, since he wanted his poetry to be a complete expression of himself, artist as well as poet. His apprenticeship in engraving probably led to the solution. At any event, each poem, starting with "Songs of Innocence," was etched on a small copper plate together with accompanying pictures or decorations growing naturally around or out of it, then transferred to paper and hand-colored. These "illuminated" sheets, brought together in paper covers, were his "books," and more beautiful ones would be hard to imagine.

This was the only form in which his poems were available, and producing them was a slow and costly process. The few that remain, usually in private collections, are vivid testimony to their beauty and uniqueness. They were never "printed" or "published" in his lifetime. The first edition of his complete works, insofar as we know, did not appear until a hundred years after his death. Small wonder he has been neglected.

It was not only the accepted forms of government, society, and religion against which Blake rebelled, but established forms of poetry as well. True, his early Songs are written in regular stanzas with due observance of rhyme and meter. But even here there is a new elasticity, bringing both tension and relaxation to the lines. One feels them responding to the touch of a master or of a liberator who wishes them to have a life of their own. In the early "Prophetic Books" that followed, he turned to blank verse, perhaps because of Milton's example, for Milton was a great influence in Blake's life. Later, when "Jerusalem" impended, Blake felt it his duty to explain in a preface the changes in his style: he was becoming an "orator."

Poet—painter—orator—prophet, Blake has been hard to classify. To many, his work has seemed either very simple or extremely opaque. He went beyond the run of poets in their surpassing ability to perceive relationships between apparently unrelated objects or ideas. He saw all as One. "Contraries are Positives," he said. "A Negation is not a Contrary . . . Without Contraries can be no Progression." Even the "Songs of Innocence" and "Songs of Experience" are not to be thought of separately but as "Shewing the Contrary States of the Human Soul." The one world concept was not strange to Blake. All was one—"one earth, one sea beneath," "one Sun each morning . . . Calling the Plowman to his Labour & the Shepherd to his Rest."

This was a simply stated belief, this oneness, but it was the base from which his thoughts and fancies took off and to which they returned. And he believed with all his heart that a man should put his whole self into his work, his life: "Energy is the only life, as it is from the body, and Reason is the bound or outward circumference of Energy." It may have been this very dedication of energy that gave such extraordinary exuberance to his creations. He had no misgivings. He was confident. He knew.

"Error is Created. Truth is Eternal. Error, or Creation, will be Burned Up [this is from 'A Vision of the Last Judgment'], & then, & not till Then, Truth or Eternity will appear. It is Burnt up the moment Men cease to behold it. I assert for My Self that I do not behold the outward Creation and that to me it is hindrance and not Action; it is as the dirt upon my feet, No part of Me. 'What,' it will be Question'd, 'When the Sun rises, do you not see a round disk of fire somewhat like a Guinea?' O no, no, I see an innumerable company of the Heavenly Host crying, 'Holy, Holy, Holy, is the Lord God Almighty.' I question not my Corporeal or Vegatative Eye any more than I should Question a Window concerning a Sight. I look thro' it & not with it."

There is Blake's sight, and his insight. His mind ranged widely and perceptively, but his feet never strayed far from their native heath. A Londoner he was born and a Londoner he remained all his days. There was one interval, which grew to three years, when he left the city and journeyed to Felpham to design and engrave plates for the compositions of other men. But this was a desert in his life, and he returned from his exile gladly at its close. He lived and died a poor man as far as worldly goods are concerned, but somehow the thought of poverty can never be associated with Blake—only the richness of his genius, which, though freely outpoured, was never lessened thereby.

PART ONE

From Poetical Sketches

TO THE MUSES

Whether on Ida's shady brow,
  Or in the chambers of the East,
The chambers of the sun, that now
  From antient melody have ceas'd;

Whether in Heav'n ye wander fair,
  Or the green corners of the earth,
Or the blue regions of the air,
  Where the melodious winds have birth;

Whether on chrystal rocks ye rove,
  Beneath the bosom of the sea
Wand'ring in many a coral grove,
  Fair Nine, forsaking Poetry!

How have you left the antient love
  That bards of old enjoy'd in you!
The languid strings do scarcely move!
  The sound is forc'd, the notes are few!

SONG

How sweet I roam'd from field to field,
  And tasted all the summer's pride,
'Till I the prince of love beheld,
  Who in the sunny beams did glide!

He shew'd me lilies for my hair,
  And blushing roses for my brow;
He led me through his gardens fair,
  Where all his golden pleasures grow.

With sweet May dews my wings were wet,
  And Phoebus fir'd my vocal rage;
He caught me in his silken net,
  And shut me in his golden cage.

He loves to sit and hear me sing,
  Then, laughing, sports and plays with me;
Then stretches out my golden wing,
  And mocks my loss of liberty.

SONG

I love the jocund dance,
  The softly-breathing song,
Where innocent eyes do glance,
  And where lisps the maiden's tongue.

I love the laughing vale,
  I love the echoing hill,
Where mirth does never fail,
  And the jolly swain laughs his fill.

I love the pleasant cot,
  I love the innocent bow'r,
Where white and brown is our lot,
  Or fruit in the mid-day hour.

I love the oaken seat,
  Beneath the oaken tree,
Where all the old villagers meet,
  And laugh our sports to see.

I love our neighbours all,
  But, Kitty, I better love thee;
And love them I ever shall;
  But thou art all to me.

SONG

Fresh from the dewy hill, the merry year
Smiles on my head, and mounts his flaming car;
Round my young brows the laurel wreathes a shade,
And rising glories beam around my head.

My feet are wing'd, while o'er the dewy lawn
I meet my maiden, risen like the morn:
Oh bless those holy feet, like angels' feet;
Oh bless those limbs, beaming with heav'nly light!

Like as an angel glitt'ring in the sky
In times of innocence and holy joy;
The joyful shepherd stops his grateful song
To hear the music of an angel's tongue.

So when she speaks, the voice of Heaven I hear:
So when we walk, nothing impure comes near;
Each field seems Eden, and each calm retreat;
Each village seems the haunt of holy feet.

But that sweet village, where my black-ey'd maid
Closes her eyes in sleep beneath night's shade,
Whene'er I enter, more than mortal fire
Burns in my soul, and does my song inspire.

From Poetical Sketches

TO SUMMER

O thou, who passest thro' our vallies in
Thy strength, curb thy fierce steeds, allay the heat
That flames from their large nostrils! thou, O Summer,
Oft pitched'st here thy golden tent, and oft
Beneath our oaks hast slept, while we beheld
With joy thy ruddy limbs and flourishing hair.

Beneath our thickest shades we oft have heard
Thy voice, when noon upon his fervid car
Rode o'er the deep of heaven; beside our springs
Sit down, and in our mossy vallies, on
Some bank beside a river clear, throw thy
Silk draperies off, and rush into the stream:
Our vallies love the Summer in his pride.

Our bards are fam'd who strike the silver wire:
Our youth are bolder than the southern swains:
Our maidens fairer in the sprightly dance:
We lack not songs, nor instruments of joy,
Nor echoes sweet, nor waters clear as heaven,
Nor laurel wreaths against the sultry heat.

TO AUTUMN

O autumn, laden with fruit, and stained
With the blood of the grape, pass not, but sit
Beneath my shady roof; there thou may'st rest,
And tune thy jolly voice to my fresh pipe;
And all the daughters of the year shall dance!
Sing now the lusty song of fruits and flowers.

"The narrow bud opens her beauties to
"The sun, and love runs in her thrilling veins;
"Blossoms hang round the brows of morning, and
"Flourish down the bright cheek of modest eve,
"Till clust'ring Summer breaks forth into singing,
"And feather'd clouds strew flowers round her head.

"The spirits of the air live on the smells
"Of fruit; and joy, with pinions light, roves round
"The gardens, or sits singing in the trees."
Thus sang the jolly Autumn as he sat;
Then rose, girded himself, and o'er the bleak
Hills fled from our sight; but left his golden load.

From Poetical Sketches

SONG

Memory, hither come,
And tune your merry notes;
And, while upon the wind
Your music floats,

I'll pore upon the stream,
Where sighing lovers dream,
And fish for fancies as they pass
Within the watery glass.

I'll drink of the clear stream,
And hear the linnet's song;
And there I'll lie and dream
The day along:

And, when night comes, I'll go
To places fit for woe,
Walking along the darken'd valley
With silent Melancholy.

SONG

My silks and fine array,
  My smiles and languish'd air,
By love are driv'n away;
  And mournful lean Despair
Brings me yew to deck my grave:
Such end true lovers have.

His face is fair as heav'n,
  When springing buds unfold;
O why to him was't giv'n,
  Whose heart is wintry cold?
His breast is love's all worship'd tomb,
Where all love's pilgrims come.

Bring me an axe and spade,
  Bring me a winding sheet;
When I my grave have made,
  Let winds and tempests beat:
Then down I'll lie, as cold as clay.
True love doth pass away!

From Poetical Sketches

TO SPRING

O thou with dewy locks, who lookest down
Thro' the clear windows of the morning, turn
Thine angel eyes upon our western isle,
Which in full choir hails thy approach, O Spring!

The hills tell each other, and the list'ning
Vallies hear; all our longing eyes are turned
Up to thy bright pavillions: issue forth,
And let thy holy feet visit our clime.

Come o'er the eastern hills, and let our winds
Kiss thy perfumed garments; let us taste
Thy morn and evening breath; scatter thy pearls
Upon our love-sick land that mourns for thee.

O deck her forth with thy fair fingers; pour
Thy soft kisses on her bosom; and put
Thy golden crown upon her languish'd head,
Whose modest tresses were bound up for thee!

TO WINTER

O Winter! bar thine adamantine doors:
The north is thine; there hast thou built thy dark
Deep-founded habitation. Shake not thy roofs,
Nor bend thy pillars with thine iron car.

He hears me not, but o'er the yawning deep
Rides heavy; his storms are unchain'd, sheathed
In ribbed steel; I dare not lift mine eyes,
For he hath rear'd his sceptre o'er the world.

Lo! now the direful monster, whose skin clings
To his strong bones, strides o'er the groaning rocks:
He withers all in silence, and his hand
Unclothes the earth, and freezes up frail life.

He takes his seat upon the cliffs; the mariner
Cries in vain. Poor little wretch! that deal'st
With storms, till heaven smiles, and the monster
Is driv'n yelling to his caves beneath mount Hecla.

From Poetical Sketches

MAD SONG

The wild winds weep,
And the night is a-cold;
Come hither, Sleep,
And my griefs infold:
But lo! the morning peeps
Over the eastern steeps,
And the rustling birds of dawn
The earth do scorn.

Lo! to the vault
Of paved heaven
With sorrow fraught
My notes are driven:
They strike the ear of night,
Make weep the eyes of day;
They make mad the roaring winds,
And with tempests play.

Like a fiend in a cloud,
With howling woe,
After night I do croud,
And with night will go;
I turn my back to the east,
From whence comforts have increas'd;
For light doth seize my brain
With frantic pain.

TO MORNING

O holy virgin! clad in purest white,
Unlock heav'n's golden gates, and issue forth;
Awake the dawn that sleeps in heaven; let light
Rise from the chambers of the east, and bring
The honied dew that cometh on waking day.
O radiant morning, salute the sun,
Rouz'd like a huntsman to the chace, and, with
Thy buskin'd feet, appear upon our hills.

TO THE EVENING STAR

Thou fair-hair'd angel of the evening,
Now, whilst the sun rests on the mountains, light
Thy bright torch of love; thy radiant crown
Put on, and smile upon our evening bed!
Smile on our loves, and, while thou drawest the
Blue curtains of the sky, scatter thy silver dew
On every flower that shuts its sweet eyes
In timely sleep. Let thy west wind sleep on
The lake; speak silence with thy glimmering eyes,
And wash the dusk with silver. Soon, full soon,
Dost thou withdraw; then the wolf rages wide,
And the lion glares thro' the dun forest:
The fleeces of our flocks are cover'd with
Thy sacred dew: protect them with thine influence.

From Poetical Sketches

PROLOGUE INTENDED FOR A DRAMATIC PIECE OF KING EDWARD THE FOURTH

O for a voice like thunder, and a tongue
To drown the throat of war!—When the senses
Are shaken, and the soul is driven to madness,
Who can stand? When the souls of the oppressed
Fight in the troubled air that rages, who can stand?
When the whirlwind of fury comes from the
Throne of God, when the frowns of his countenance
Drive the nations together, who can stand?
When Sin claps his broad wings over the battle,
And sails rejoicing in the flood of Death;
When souls are torn to everlasting fire,
And fiends of Hell rejoice upon the slain,
O who can stand? O who hath caused this?
O who can answer at the throne of God?
The Kings and Nobles of the Land have done it!
Hear it not, Heaven, thy Ministers have done it!

PART TWO

Songs of Innocence and of Experience

Songs of Innocence

INTRODUCTION

Piping down the valleys wild,
Piping songs of pleasant glee,
On a cloud I saw a child,
And he laughing said to me:

"Pipe a song about a Lamb!"
So I piped with merry chear.
"Piper, pipe that song again;"
So I piped: he wept to hear.

"Drop thy pipe, thy happy pipe,
"Sing thy songs of happy chear:"
So I sung the same again,
While he wept with joy to hear.

"Piper, sit thee down and write
"In a book that all may read."
So he vanish'd from my sight,
And I pluck'd a hollow reed,

And I made a rural pen,
And I stain'd the water clear,
And I wrote my happy songs
Every child may joy to hear.

A DREAM

Once a dream did weave a shade
O'er my Angel-guarded bed,
That an Emmet lost its way
Where on grass methought I lay.

Troubled, 'wilder'd, and forlorn,
Dark, benighted, travel-worn,
Over many a tangled spray,
All heart-broke I heard her say:

"O, my children! do they cry?
"Do they hear their father sigh?
"Now they look abroad to see:
"Now return and weep for me."

Pitying, I drop'd a tear;
But I saw a glow-worm near,
Who replied: "What wailing wight
"Calls the watchman of the night?

"I am set to light the ground,
"While the beetle goes his round:
"Follow now the beetle's hum;
"Little wanderer, hie thee home."

THE LITTLE GIRL LOST

In futurity
I prophetic see
That the earth from sleep
(Grave the sentence deep)

Shall arise and seek
For her maker meek;
And the desart wild
Become a garden mild.

In the southern clime,
Where the summer's prime
Never fades away,
Lovely Lyca lay.

Seven summers old
Lovely Lyca told;
She had wander'd long
Hearing wild birds' song.

"Sweet sleep, come to me
"Underneath this tree.
"Do father, mother weep,
"Where can Lyca sleep?

"Lost in desart wild
"Is your little child.
"How can Lyca sleep
"If her mother weep?

"If her heart does ake
"Then let Lyca wake;
"If my mother sleep,
"Lyca shall not weep.

"Frowning, frowning night,
"O'er this desart bright
"Let thy moon arise
"While I close my eyes."

Sleeping Lyca lay
While the beasts of prey,
Come from caverns deep,
View'd the maid asleep.

The kingly lion stood
And the virgin view'd,
Then he gambol'd round
O'er the hallow'd ground.

Leopards, tygers, play
Round her as she lay,
While the lion old
Bow'd his mane of gold

And her bosom lick,
And upon her neck
From his eyes of flame
Ruby tears there came;

While the lioness
Loos'd her slender dress,
And naked they convey'd
To caves the sleeping maid.

THE LITTLE GIRL FOUND

All the night in woe
Lyca's parents go
Over vallies deep,
While the desarts weep.

Tired and woe-begone,
Hoarse with making moan,
Arm in arm seven days
They trac'd the desart ways.

Seven nights they sleep
Among shadows deep,
And dream they see their child
Starv'd in desart wild.

Pale, thro' pathless ways
The fancied image strays
Famish'd, weeping, weak,
With hollow piteous shriek.

Rising from unrest,
The trembling woman prest
With feet of weary woe:
She could no further go.

In his arms he bore
Her, arm'd with sorrow sore;
Till before their way
A couching lion lay.

Turning back was vain:
Soon his heavy mane
Bore them to the ground.
Then he stalk'd around,

Smelling to his prey;
But their fears allay
When he licks their hands,
And silent by them stands.

They look upon his eyes
Fill'd with deep surprise,
And wondering behold
A Spirit arm'd in gold.

On his head a crown,
On his shoulders down
Flow'd his golden hair.
Gone was all their care.

"Follow me," he said;
"Weep not for the maid;
"In my palace deep
"Lyca lies asleep."

Then they followed
Where the vision led,
And saw their sleeping child
Among tygers wild.

To this day they dwell
In a lonely dell;
Nor fear the wolvish howl
Nor the lions' growl.

THE LAMB

Little Lamb, who made thee?
Dost thou know who made thee?
Gave thee life, & bid thee feed
By the stream & o'er the mead;
Gave thee clothing of delight,
Softest clothing, wooly, bright;
Gave thee such a tender voice,
Making all the vales rejoice?
Little Lamb, who made thee?
Dost thou know who made thee?

Little Lamb, I'll tell thee,
Little Lamb, I'll tell thee:
He is called by thy name,
For he calls himself a Lamb.
He is meek, & he is mild;

He became a little child.
I a child, & thou a lamb,
We are called by his name.
Little Lamb, God bless thee!
Little Lamb, God bless thee!

THE ECCHOING GREEN

The Sun does arise,
And make happy the skies;
The merry bells ring
To welcome the Spring;
The skylark and thrush,
The birds of the bush,
Sing louder around
To the bells' chearful sound,
While our sports shall be seen
On the Ecchoing Green.

Old John, with white hair,
Does laugh away care,
Sitting under the oak,
Among the old folk.
They laugh at our play,
And soon they all say:
"Such, such were the joys
"When we all, girls & boys,
"In our youth time were seen
"On the Ecchoing Green."

Till the little ones, weary,
No more can be merry;
The sun does descend,
And our sports have an end.
Round the laps of their mothers
Many sisters and brothers,
Like birds in their nest,
Are ready for rest,
And sport no more seen
On the darkening Green.

THE BLOSSOM

Merry, Merry Sparrow!
Under leaves so green
A happy Blossom
Sees you swift as arrow
Seek your cradle narrow
Near my Bosom.

Pretty, Pretty Robin!
Under leaves so green
A happy Blossom
Hears you sobbing, sobbing,
Pretty, Pretty Robin,
Near my Bosom.

THE DIVINE IMAGE

To Mercy, Pity, Peace, and Love
All pray in their distress;
And to these virtues of delight
Return their thankfulness.

For Mercy, Pity, Peace, and Love
Is God, our father dear,
And Mercy, Pity, Peace, and Love
Is Man, his child and care.

For Mercy has a human heart,
Pity a human face,
And Love, the human form divine,
And Peace, the human dress.

Then every man, of every clime,
That prays in his distress,
Prays to the human form divine,
Love, Mercy, Pity, Peace.

And all must love the human form,
In heathen, turk, or jew;
Where Mercy, Love, & Pity dwell
There God is dwelling too.

THE CHIMNEY SWEEPER

When my mother died I was very young,
And my Father sold me while yet my tongue
Could scarcely cry "'weep! 'weep! 'weep! 'weep!"
So your chimneys I sweep, & in soot I sleep.

There's little Tom Dacre, who cried when his head,
That curl'd like a lamb's back, was shav'd: so I said
"Hush, Tom! never mind it, for when your head's bare
"You know that the soot cannot spoil your white hair."

And so he was quiet, & that very night,
As Tom was a-sleeping, he had such a sight!
That thousands of sweepers, Dick, Joe, Ned, & Jack,
Were all of them lock'd up in coffins of black.

And by came an Angel who had a bright key,
And he open'd the coffins & set them all free;
Then down a green plain leaping, laughing, they run,
And wash in a river, and shine in the Sun.

Then naked & white, all their bags left behind,
They rise upon clouds and sport in the wind;
And the Angel told Tom, if he'd be a good boy,
He'd have God for his father, & never want joy.

And so Tom awoke; and we rose in the dark,
And got with our bags & our brushes to work.
Tho' the morning was cold, Tom was happy & warm;
So if all do their duty they need not fear harm.

NURSE'S SONG

When the voices of children are heard on the green
And laughing is heard on the hill,
My heart is at rest within my breast
And everything else is still.

"Then come home, my children, the sun is gone down
"And the dews of night arise;
"Come, come, leave off play, and let us away
"Till the morning appears in the skies."

"No, no, let us play, for it is yet day
"And we cannot go to sleep;
"Besides, in the sky the little birds fly
"And the hills are all cover'd with sheep."

"Well, well, go & play till the light fades away
"And then go home to bed."
The little ones leaped & shouted & laugh'd
And all the hills ecchoed.

INFANT JOY

"I have no name:
"I am but two days old."
What shall I call thee?
"I happy am,
"Joy is my name."
Sweet joy befall thee!

Pretty joy!
Sweet joy but two days old,
Sweet joy I call thee:
Thou dost smile,
I sing the while,
Sweet joy befall thee!

THE SHEPHERD

How sweet is the Shepherd's sweet lot!
From the morn to the evening he strays;
He shall follow his sheep all the day,
And his tongue shall be filled with praise.

For he hears the lamb's innocent call,
And he hears the ewe's tender reply;
He is watchful while they are in peace,
For they know when their Shepherd is nigh.

NIGHT

The sun descending in the west,
The evening star does shine;
The birds are silent in their nest,
And I must seek for mine.
The moon like a flower
In heaven's high bower,
With silent delight
Sits and smiles on the night.

Farewell, green fields and happy groves,
Where flocks have took delight.
Where lambs have nibbled, silent moves
The feet of angels bright;
Unseen they pour blessing
And joy without ceasing,
On each bud and blossom,
And each sleeping bosom.

They look in every thoughtless nest,
Where birds are cover'd warm;
They visit caves of every beast,
To keep them all from harm.
If they see any weeping
That should have been sleeping,
They pour sleep on their head,
And sit down by their bed.

When wolves and tygers howl for prey,
They pitying stand and weep;
Seeking to drive their thirst away,
And keep them from the sheep;
But if they rush dreadful,
The angels, most heedful,
Receive each mild spirit,
New worlds to inherit.

And there the lion's ruddy eyes
Shall flow with tears of gold,
And pitying the tender cries,
And walking round the fold,
Saying "Wrath, by his meekness,
"And by his health, sickness
"Is driven away
"From our immortal day.

"And now beside thee, bleating lamb,
"I can lie down and sleep;
"Or think on him who bore thy name,
"Graze after thee and weep.
"For, wash'd in life's river,
"My bright mane for ever
"Shall shine like the gold
"As I guard o'er the fold."

A CRADLE SONG

Sweet dreams, form a shade
O'er my lovely infant's head;
Sweet dreams of pleasant streams
By happy, silent, moony beams.

Sweet sleep, with soft down
Weave thy brows an infant crown.
Sweet sleep, Angel mild,
Hover o'er my happy child.

Sweet smiles, in the night
Hover over my delight;
Sweet smiles, Mother's smiles,
All the livelong night beguiles.

Sweet moans, dovelike sighs,
Chase not slumber from thy eyes.
Sweet moans, sweeter smiles,
All the dovelike moans beguiles.

Sleep, sleep, happy child,
All creation slept and smil'd;
Sleep, sleep, happy sleep,
While o'er thee thy mother weep.

Sweet babe, in thy face
Holy image I can trace.
Sweet babe, once like thee,
Thy maker lay and wept for me,

Wept for me, for thee, for all,
When he was an infant small.
Thou his image ever see,
Heavenly face that smiles on thee,

Smiles on thee, on me, on all;
Who became an infant small.
Infant smiles are his own smiles;
Heaven & earth to peace beguiles.

THE LITTLE BOY LOST

"Father! father! where are you going?
"O do not walk so fast.
"Speak, father, speak to your little boy,
"Or else I shall be lost."

The night was dark, no father was there;
The child was wet with dew;
The mire was deep, & the child did weep,
And away the vapour flew.

THE LITTLE BOY FOUND

The little boy lost in the lonely fen,
Led by the wand'ring light,
Began to cry; but God, ever nigh,
Appear'd like his father in white.

He kissed the child & by the hand led
And to his mother brought,
Who in sorrow pale, thro' the lonely dale,
Her little boy weeping sought.

HOLY THURSDAY

'Twas on a Holy Thursday, their innocent faces clean,
The children walking two & two, in red & blue & green,
Grey-headed beadles walk'd before, with wands as white as
 snow,
Till into the high dome of Paul's they like Thames' waters
 flow.

O what a multitude they seem'd, these flowers of London
 town!
Seated in companies they sit with radiance all their own.
The hum of multitudes was there, but multitudes of lambs,
Thousands of little boys & girls raising their innocent hands.

Now like a mighty wind they raise to heaven the voice of
 song,
Or like harmonious thunderings the seats of Heaven among.
Beneath them sit the aged men, wise guardians of the poor;
Then cherish pity, lest you drive an angel from your door.

ON ANOTHER'S SORROW

Can I see another's woe,
And not be in sorrow too?
Can I see another's grief,
And not seek for kind relief?

Can I see a falling tear,
And not feel my sorrow's share?
Can a father see his child
Weep, nor be with sorrow fill'd?

Can a mother sit and hear
An infant groan, an infant fear?
No, no! never can it be!
Never, never can it be!

And can he who smiles on all
Hear the wren with sorrows small,
Hear the small bird's grief & care,
Hear the woes that infants bear,

And not sit beside the nest,
Pouring pity in their breast;
And not sit the cradle near,
Weeping tear on infant's tear;

And not sit both night & day,
Wiping all our tears away?
O! no never can it be!
Never, never can it be!

He doth give his joy to all;
He becomes an infant small;
He becomes a man of woe;
He doth feel the sorrow too.

Think not thou canst sigh a sigh
And thy maker is not by;
Think not thou canst weep a tear
And thy maker is not near.

O! he gives to us his joy
That our grief he may destroy;
Till our grief is fled & gone
He doth sit by us and moan.

SPRING

Sound the Flute!
Now it's mute.
Birds delight
Day and Night;
Nightingale
In the dale,
Lark in Sky,
Merrily,
Merrily, Merrily, to welcome in the Year.

Little Boy,
Full of joy;
Little Girl,
Sweet and small;
Cock does crow,
So do you;
Merry voice,
Infant noise,
Merrily, Merrily, to welcome in the Year.

Little Lamb,
Here I am;
Come and lick
My white neck;

Let me pull
Your soft Wool;
Let me kiss
Your soft face:
Merrily, Merrily, we welcome in the Year.

THE VOICE OF THE ANCIENT BARD

Youth of delight, come hither,
And see the opening morn,
Image of truth new born.
Doubt is fled, & clouds of reason,
Dark disputes & artful teazing.
Folly is an endless maze,
Tangled roots perplex her ways.
How many have fallen there!
They stumble all night over bones of the dead,
And feel they know not what but care,
And wish to lead others, when they should be led.

THE LITTLE BLACK BOY

My mother bore me in the southern wild,
And I am black, but O! my soul is white;
White as an angel is the English child,
But I am black, as if bereav'd of light.

My mother taught me underneath a tree,
And sitting down before the heat of day,
She took me on her lap and kissed me,
And pointing to the east, began to say:

"Look on the rising sun: there God does live,
"And gives his light, and gives his heat away;
"And flowers and trees and beasts and men recieve
"Comfort in morning, joy in the noonday.

"And we are put on earth a little space,
"That we may learn to bear the beams of love;
"And these black bodies and this sunburnt face
"Is but a cloud, and like a shady grove.

"For when our souls have learn'd the heat to bear,
"The cloud will vanish; we shall hear his voice,
"Saying: 'Come out from the grove, my love & care,
" 'And round my golden tent like lambs rejoice.' "

Thus did my mother say, and kissed me;
And thus I say to little English boy.
When I from black and he from white cloud free,
And round the tent of God like lambs we joy,

I'll shade him from the heat, till he can bear
To lean in joy upon our father's knee;
And then I'll stand and stroke his silver hair,
And be like him, and he will then love me.

THE SCHOOL BOY

I love to rise in a summer morn
When the birds sing on every tree;
The distant huntsman winds his horn,
And the sky-lark sings with me.
O! what sweet company.

But to go to school in a summer morn,
O! it drives all joy away;
Under a cruel eye outworn,
The little ones spend the day
In sighing and dismay.

Ah! then at times I drooping sit,
And spend many an anxious hour,
Nor in my book can I take delight,
Nor sit in learning's bower,
Worn thro' with the dreary shower.

How can the bird that is born for joy
Sit in a cage and sing?
How can a child, when fears annoy,
But droop his tender wing,
And forget his youthful spring?

O! father & mother, if buds are nip'd
And blossoms blown away,
And if the tender plants are strip'd
Of their joy in the springing day,
By sorrow and care's dismay,

How shall the summer arise in joy,
Or the summer fruits appear?
Or how shall we gather what griefs destroy,
Or bless the mellowing year,
When the blasts of winter appear?

LAUGHING SONG

When the green woods laugh with the voice of joy,
And the dimpling stream runs laughing by;
When the air does laugh with our merry wit,
And the green hill laughs with the noise of it;

When the meadows laugh with lively green,
And the grasshopper laughs in the merry scene,
When Mary and Susan and Emily
With their sweet round mouths sing "Ha, Ha, He!"

When the painted birds laugh in the shade,
Where our table with cherries and nuts is spread,
Come live & be merry, and join with me,
To sing the sweet chorus of "Ha, Ha, He!"

Songs of Experience

INTRODUCTION

Hear the voice of the Bard!
Who Present, Past, & Future, sees;
Whose ears have heard
The Holy Word
That walk'd among the ancient trees,

Calling the lapsed Soul,
And weeping in the evening dew;
That might controll
The starry pole,
And fallen, fallen light renew!

"O Earth, O Earth, return!
"Arise from out the dewy grass;
"Night is worn,
"And the morn
"Rises from the slumberous mass.

"Turn away no more;
"Why wilt thou turn away?
"The starry floor,
"The wat'ry shore,
"Is giv'n thee till the break of day."

EARTH'S ANSWER

Earth rais'd up her head
From the darkness dread & drear.
Her light fled,
Stony dread!
And her locks cover'd with grey despair.

"Prison'd on wat'ry shore,
"Starry Jealousy does keep my den:
"Cold and hoar,
"Weeping o'er,
"I hear the Father of the ancient men.

"Selfish father of men!
"Cruel, jealous, selfish fear!
"Can delight,
"Chain'd in night,
"The virgins of youth and morning bear?

"Does spring hide its joy
"When buds and blossoms grow?
"Does the sower
"Sow by night,
"Or the plowman in darkness plow?

"Break this heavy chain
"That does freeze my bones around.
"Selfish! vain!
"Eternal bane!
"That free Love with bondage bound."

THE CHIMNEY SWEEPER

A little black thing among the snow,
Crying "'weep! 'weep!" in notes of woe!
"Where are thy father & mother? say?"
"They are both gone up to the church to pray.

"Because I was happy upon the heath,
"And smil'd among the winter's snow,
"They clothed me in the clothes of death,
"And taught me to sing the notes of woe.

"And because I am happy & dance & sing,
"They think they have done me no injury,
"And are gone to praise God & his Priest & King,
"Who make up a heaven of our misery."

THE FLY

Little Fly,
Thy summer's play
My thoughtless hand
Has brush'd away.

Am not I
A fly like thee?
Or art not thou
A man like me?

For I dance,
And drink, & sing,
Till some blind hand
Shall brush my wing.

If thought is life
And strength & breath,
And the want
Of thought is death;

Then am I
A happy fly,
If I live
Or if I die.

HOLY THURSDAY

Is this a holy thing to see
In a rich and fruitful land,
Babes reduc'd to misery,
Fed with cold and usurous hand?

Is that trembling cry a song?
Can it be a song of joy?
And so many children poor?
It is a land of poverty!

And their sun does never shine,
And their fields are bleak & bare,
And their ways are fill'd with thorns:
It is eternal winter there.

For where-e'er the sun does shine,
And where-e'er the rain does fall,
Babe can never hunger there,
Nor poverty the mind appall.

THE ANGEL

I Dreamt a Dream! what can it mean?
And that I was a maiden Queen,
Guarded by an Angel mild:
Witless woe was ne'er beguil'd!

And I wept both night and day,
And he wip'd my tears away,
And I wept both day and night,
And hid from him my heart's delight.

So he took his wings and fled;
Then the morn blush'd rosy red;
I dried my tears, & arm'd my fears
With ten thousand shields and spears.

Soon my Angel came again:
I was arm'd, he came in vain;
For the time of youth was fled,
And grey hairs were on my head.

THE TYGER

Tyger! Tyger! burning bright
In the forests of the night,
What immortal hand or eye
Could frame thy fearful symmetry?

In what distant deeps or skies
Burnt the fire of thine eyes?
On what wings dare he aspire?
What the hand dare sieze the fire?

And what shoulder, & what art,
Could twist the sinews of thy heart?
And when thy heart began to beat,
What dread hand? & what dread feet?

What the hammer? what the chain?
In what furnace was thy brain?
What the anvil? what dread grasp
Dare its deadly terrors clasp?

When the stars threw down their spears,
And water'd heaven with their tears,
Did he smile his work to see?
Did he who made the Lamb make thee?

Tyger! Tyger! burning bright
In the forests of the night,
What immortal hand or eye,
Dare frame thy fearful symmetry?

THE CLOD & THE PEBBLE

"Love seeketh not Itself to please,
"Nor for itself hath any care,
"But for another gives its ease,
"And builds a Heaven in Hell's despair."

So sang a little Clod of Clay
Trodden with the cattle's feet,
But a Pebble of the brook
Warbled out these metres meet:

"Love seeketh only Self to please,
"To bind another to Its delight,
"Joys in another's loss of ease,
"And builds a Hell in Heaven's despite."

MY PRETTY ROSE TREE

A flower was offer'd to me,
Such a flower as May never bore;
But I said "I've a Pretty Rose-tree,"
And I passed the sweet flower o'er.

Then I went to my Pretty Rose-tree,
To tend her by day and by night;
But my Rose turn'd away with jealousy,
And her thorns were my only delight.

AH! SUN-FLOWER

Ah, Sun-flower, weary of time,
Who countest the steps of the Sun,
Seeking after that sweet golden clime
Where the traveller's journey is done:

Where the Youth pined away with desire,
And the pale Virgin shrouded in snow
Arise from their graves, and aspire
Where my Sun-flower wishes to go.

THE SICK ROSE

O Rose, thou art sick!
The invisible worm
That flies in the night,
In the howling storm,

Has found out thy bed
Of crimson joy:
And his dark secret love
Does thy life destroy.

NURSE'S SONG

When the voices of children are heard on the green
And whisp'rings are in the dale,
The days of my youth rise fresh in my mind,
My face turns green and pale.

Then come home, my children, the sun is gone down,
And the dews of night arise;
Your spring & your day are wasted in play,
And your winter and night in disguise.

THE GARDEN OF LOVE

I went to the Garden of Love,
And saw what I never had seen:
A Chapel was built in the midst,
Where I used to play on the green.

And the gates of this Chapel were shut,
And "Thou shalt not" writ over the door;
So I turn'd to the Garden of Love
That so many sweet flowers bore;

And I saw it was filled with graves,
And tomb-stones where flowers should be;
And Priests in black gowns were walking their rounds,
And binding with briars my joys & desires.

THE LILLY

The modest Rose puts forth a thorn,
The humble Sheep a threat'ning horn;
While the Lilly white shall in Love delight,
Nor a thorn, nor a threat, stain her beauty bright.

THE LITTLE VAGABOND

Dear Mother, dear Mother, the Church is cold,
But the Ale-house is healthy & pleasant & warm;
Besides I can tell where I am used well,
Such usage in Heaven will never do well.

But if at the Church they would give us some Ale,
And a pleasant fire our souls to regale,
We'd sing and we'd pray all the live-long day,
Nor ever once wish from the Church to stray.

Then the Parson might preach, & drink, & sing,
And we'd be as happy as birds in the spring;
And modest dame Lurch, who is always at Church,
Would not have bandy children, nor fasting, nor birch.

And God, like a father rejoicing to see
His children as pleasant and happy as he,
Would have no more quarrel with the Devil or the
    Barrel,
But kiss him, & give him both drink and apparel.

LONDON

I wander thro' each charter'd street,
Near where the charter'd Thames does flow,
And mark in every face I meet
Marks of weakness, marks of woe.

In every cry of every Man,
In every Infant's cry of fear,
In every voice, in every ban,
The mind-forg'd manacles I hear.

How the Chimney-sweeper's cry
Every black'ning Church appalls;
And the hapless Soldier's sigh
Runs in blood down Palace walls.

But most thro' midnight streets I hear
How the youthful Harlot's curse
Blasts the new born Infant's tear,
And blights with plagues the Marriage hearse.

THE HUMAN ABSTRACT

Pity would be no more
If we did not make somebody Poor;
And Mercy no more could be
If all were as happy as we.

And mutual fear brings peace,
Till the selfish loves increase:
Then Cruelty knits a snare,
And spreads his baits with care.

He sits down with holy fears,
And waters the ground with tears;
Then Humility takes its root
Underneath his foot.

Soon spreads the dismal shade
Of Mystery over his head;
And the Catterpillar and Fly
Feed on the Mystery.

And it bears the fruit of Deceit,
Ruddy and sweet to eat;
And the Raven his nest has made
In its thickest shade.

The Gods of the earth and sea
Sought thro' Nature to find this Tree;
But their search was all in vain:
There grows one in the Human Brain.

INFANT SORROW

My mother groan'd! my father wept.
Into the dangerous world I leapt:
Helpless, naked, piping loud:
Like a fiend hid in a cloud.

Struggling in my father's hands,
Striving against my swadling bands.
Bound and weary I thought best
To sulk upon my mother's breast.

A POISON TREE

I was angry with my friend:
I told my wrath, my wrath did end.
I was angry with my foe:
I told it not, my wrath did grow.

And I water'd it in fears,
Night & morning with my tears;
And I sunned it with smiles,
And with soft deceitful wiles.

And it grew both day and night,
Till it bore an apple bright;
And my foe beheld it shine,
And he knew that it was mine,

And into my garden stole
When the night had veil'd the pole:
In the morning glad I see
My foe outstretch'd beneath the tree.

A LITTLE BOY LOST

"Nought loves another as itself,
"Nor venerates another so,
"Nor is it possible to Thought
"A greater than itself to know:

"And Father, how can I love you
"Or any of my brothers more?
"I love you like the little bird
"That picks up crumbs around the door."

The Priest sat by and heard the child,
In trembling zeal he siez'd his hair:
He led him by his little coat,
And all admir'd the Priestly care.

And standing on the altar high,
"Lo! what a fiend is here!" said he,
"One who sets reason up for judge
"Of our most holy Mystery."

The weeping child could not be heard,
The weeping parents wept in vain;
They strip'd him to his little shirt,
And bound him in an iron chain;

And burn'd him in a holy place,
Where many had been burn'd before:
The weeping parents wept in vain.
Are such things done on Albion's shore?

A LITTLE GIRL LOST

Children of the future Age
Reading this indignant page,
Know that in a former time
Love! sweet Love! was thought a crime.

In the Age of Gold,
Free from winter's cold,
Youth and maiden bright
To the holy light,
Naked in the sunny beams delight.

Once a youthful pair,
Fill'd with softest care,
Met in garden bright
Where the holy light
Had just remov'd the curtains of the night.

There, in rising day,
On the grass they play;
Parents were afar,
Strangers came not near,
And the maiden soon forgot her fear.

Tired with kisses sweet,
They agree to meet
When the silent sleep
Waves o'er heaven's deep,
And the weary tired wanderers weep.

To her father white
Came the maiden bright;
But his loving look,
Like the holy book,
All her tender limbs with terror shook.

"Ona! pale and weak!
"To thy father speak:
"O, the trembling fear!
"O, the dismal care!
"That shakes the blossoms of my hoary hair."

A DIVINE IMAGE

Cruelty has a Human Heart,
And Jealousy a Human Face;
Terror the Human Form Divine,
And Secrecy the Human Dress.

The Human Dress is forged Iron,
The Human Form a fiery Forge,
The Human Face a Furnace seal'd,
The Human Heart its hungry Gorge.

PART THREE

Verses and Fragments

I HEARD AN ANGEL SINGING

I heard an Angel singing
When the day was springing,
"Mercy, Pity, Peace
"Is the world's release."

Thus he sung all day
Over the new mown hay,
Till the sun went down
And haycocks looked brown.

I heard a Devil curse
Over the heath & the furze,
"Mercy could be no more,
"If there was nobody poor,

"And pity no more could be,
"If all were as happy as we."
At his curse the sun went down,
And the heavens gave a frown.

Down pour'd the heavy rain
Over the new reap'd grain . . .
And Miseries' increase
Is Mercy, Pity, Peace.

A CRADLE SONG

Sleep, Sleep, beauty bright
Dreaming o'er the joys of night.
Sleep, Sleep: in thy sleep
Little sorrows sit & weep.

Sweet Babe, in thy face
Soft desires I can trace
Secret joys & secret smiles
Little pretty infant wiles.

As thy softest limbs I feel
Smiles as of the morning steal
O'er thy cheek & o'er thy breast
Where thy little heart does rest.

O, the cunning wiles that creep
In thy little heart asleep.
When thy little heart does wake,
Then the dreadful lightnings break.

From thy cheek & from thy eye
O'er the youthful harvests nigh
Infant wiles & infant smiles
Heaven & Earth of peace beguiles.

THE LAND OF DREAMS

Awake, awake, my little Boy!
Thou wast thy Mother's only joy;
Why dost thou weep in thy gentle sleep?
Awake! thy Father does thee keep.

"O, what Land is the Land of Dreams?
"What are its Mountains & what are its Streams?
"O Father, I saw my Mother there,
"Among the Lillies by waters fair.

"Among the Lambs, clothed in white,
"She walk'd with her Thomas in sweet delight.
"I wept for joy, like a dove I mourn;
"O! when shall I again return?"

Dear Child, I also by pleasant Streams
Have wander'd all Night in the Land of Dreams;
But tho' calm & warm the waters wide,
I could not get to the other side.

"Father, O Father! what do we here
"In this Land of unbelief & fear?
"The Land of Dreams is better far,
"Above the light of the Morning Star."

ARE NOT THE JOYS OF MORNING SWEETER?

Are not the joys of morning sweeter
Than the joys of night?
And are the vig'rous joys of youth
Ashamed of the light?

Let age & sickness silent rob
The vineyards in the night;
But those who burn with vig'rous youth
Pluck fruits before the light.

LOVE TO FAULTS IS ALWAYS BLIND

Love to faults is always blind,
Always is to joy inclin'd,
Lawless, wing'd, & unconfin'd,
And breaks all chains from every mind.

Deceit to secresy confin'd,
Lawful, cautious, & refin'd;
To every thing but interest blind,
And forges fetters for the mind.

THE WILD FLOWER'S SONG

As I wander'd the forest,
The green leaves among,
I heard a wild flower
Singing a song:

"I slept in the dark
"In the silent night,
"I murmur'd my fears
"And I felt delight.

"In the morning I went
"As rosy as morn
"To seek for new Joy,
"But I met with scorn."

MOCK ON, MOCK ON VOLTAIRE, ROUSSEAU

Mock on, Mock on Voltaire, Rousseau:
Mock on, Mock on: 'tis all in vain!
You throw the sand against the wind,
And the wind blows it back again.

And every sand becomes a Gém
Reflected in the beams divine;
Blown back they blind the mocking Eye,
But still in Israel's paths they shine.

The Atoms of Democritus
And Newton's Particles of light
Are sands upon the Red sea shore,
Where Israel's tents do shine so bright.

NEVER PAIN TO TELL THY LOVE

Never pain to tell thy love
Love that never told can be;
For the gentle wind does move
Silently, invisibly.

I told my love, I told my love,
I told her all my heart,
Trembling, cold, in ghastly fears—
Ah, she doth depart.

Soon as she was gone from me
A traveller came by
Silently, invisibly—
O, was no deny.

The Angel that presided o'er my birth
Said, "Little creature, form'd of Joy & Mirth,
"Go love without the help of any Thing on Earth."

Terror in the house does roar,
But Pity stands before the door.

AUGURIES OF INNOCENCE

To see a World in a Grain of Sand
And a Heaven in a Wild Flower,
Hold Infinity in the palm of your hand
And Eternity in an hour.

A Robin Red breast in a Cage
Puts all Heaven in a Rage.
A dove house fill'd with doves & Pigeons
Shudders Hell thro' all its regions.
A dog starv'd at his Master's Gate
Predicts the ruin of the State.
A Horse misus'd upon the Road
Calls to Heaven for Human blood.
Each outcry of the hunted Hare
A fibre from the Brain does tear.
A Skylark wounded in the wing,
A Cherubim does cease to sing.
The Game Cock clip'd & arm'd for fight
Does the Rising Sun affright.
Every Wolf's & Lion's howl
Raises from Hell a Human Soul.
The wild deer, wand'ring here & there,
Keeps the Human Soul from Care.
The Lamb misus'd breeds Public strife
And yet forgives the Butcher's Knife.
The Bat that flits at close of Eve

Has left the Brain that won't Believe.
The Owl that calls upon the Night
Speaks the Unbeliever's fright.
He who shall hurt the little Wren
Shall never be belov'd by Men.
He who the Ox to wrath has mov'd
Shall never be by Woman lov'd.
The wanton Boy that kills the Fly
Shall feel the Spider's enmity.
He who torments the Chafer's sprite
Weaves a Bower in endless Night.
The Catterpiller on the Leaf
Repeats to thee thy Mother's grief.
Kill not the Moth nor Butterfly,
For the Last Judgment draweth nigh.
He who shall train the Horse to War
Shall never pass the Polar Bar.
The Beggar's Dog & Widow's Cat,
Feed them & thou wilt grow fat.
The Gnat that sings his Summer's song
Poison gets from Slander's tongue.
The poison of the Snake & Newt
Is the sweat of Envy's Foot.
The Poison of the Honey Bee
Is the Artist's Jealousy.
The Prince's Robes & Beggar's Rags
Are Toadstools on the Miser's Bags.
A truth that's told with bad intent

Beats all the Lies you can invent.
It is right it should be so;
Man was made for Joy & Woe;
And when this we rightly know
Thro' the World we safely go.
Joy & Woe are woven fine,
A Clothing for the Soul divine;
Under every grief & pine
Runs a joy with silken twine.
The Babe is more than swadling Bands;
Throughout all these Human Lands
Tools were made, & Born were hands,
Every Farmer Understands.
Every Tear in Every Eye
Becomes a Babe in Eternity;
This is caught by Females bright
And return'd to its own delight.
The Bleat, the Bark, Bellow & Roar
Are Waves that Beat on Heaven's Shore.
The Babe that weeps the Rod beneath
Writes Revenge in realms of death.
The Beggar's Rags, fluttering in Air,
Does to Rags the Heavens tear.
The Soldier, arm'd with Sword & Gun,
Palsied strikes the Summer's Sun.
The poor Man's Farthing is worth more
Than all the Gold on Afric's Shore.
One Mite wrung from the Labrer's hands

Shall buy & sell the Miser's Lands:
Or, if protected from on high,
Does that whole Nation sell & buy.
He who mocks the Infant's Faith
Shall be mock'd in Age & Death.
He who shall teach the Child to Doubt
The rotting Grave shall ne'er get out.
He who respects the Infant's faith
Triumphs over Hell & Death.
The Child's Toys & the Old Man's Reasons
Are the Fruits of the Two seasons.
The Questioner, who sits so sly,
Shall never know how to Reply.
He who replies to words of Doubt
Doth put the Light of Knowledge out.
The Strongest Poison ever known
Came from Caesar's Laurel Crown.
Nought can deform the Human Race
Like to the Armour's iron brace.
When Gold & Gems adorn the Plow
To peaceful Arts shall Envy Bow.
A Riddle or the Cricket's Cry
Is to Doubt a fit Reply.
The Emmet's Inch & Eagle's Mile
Make Lame Philosophy to smile.
He who Doubts from what he sees

Will ne'er Believe, do what you Please.
If the Sun & Moon should doubt,
They'd immediately Go out.
To be in a Passion you Good may do,
But no Good if a Passion is in you.
The Whore & Gambler, by the State
Licenc'd, build that Nation's Fate.
The Harlot's cry from Street to Street
Shall weave Old England's winding Sheet.
The Winner's Shout, the Loser's Curse,
Dance before dead England's Hearse.
Every Night & every Morn
Some to Misery are Born.
Every Morn & every Night
Some are Born to sweet delight.
Some are Born to sweet delight,
Some are Born to Endless Night.
We are led to Believe a Lie
When we see not Thro' the Eye
Which was Born in a Night to perish in a Night
When the Soul Slept in Beams of Light.
God Appears & God is Light
To those poor Souls who dwell in Night,
But does a Human Form Display
To those who Dwell in Realms of day.

THE SWORD SUNG ON THE BARREN HEATH

The sword sung on the barren heath,
The sickle in the fruitful field:
The sword he sung a song of death,
But could not make the sickle yield.

IF YOU TRAP THE MOMENT BEFORE IT'S RIPE

If you trap the moment before it's ripe,
The tears of repentence you'll certainly wipe;
But if once you let the ripe moment go
You can never wipe off the tears of woe.

ETERNITY

He who bends to himself a joy
Does the winged life destroy;
But he who kisses the joy as it flies
Lives in eternity's sun rise.

RICHES

The countless gold of a merry heart,
The rubies & pearls of a loving eye,
The indolent never can bring to the mart,
Nor the secret hoard up in his treasury.

AN ANSWER TO THE PARSON

"Why of the sheep do you not learn peace?"
"Because I don't want you to shear my fleece."

WHY SHOULD I CARE FOR THE MEN OF THAMES?

Why should I care for the men of thames,
Or the cheating waves of charter'd streams,
Or shrink at the little blasts of fear
That the hireling blows into my ear?

Tho' born on the cheating banks of Thames,
Tho' his waters bathed my infant limbs,
The Ohio shall wash his stains from me:
I was born a slave, but I go to be free.

THE GREY MONK

"I die, I die!" the Mother said,
"My Children die for lack of Bread.
"What more has the merciless Tyrant said?"
The Monk sat down on the Stony Bed.

The blood red ran from the Grey Monk's side,
His hands & feet were wounded wide,
His Body bent, his arms & knees
Like to the roots of ancient trees.

His eye was dry; no tear could flow:
A hollow groan first spoke his woe.
He trembled & shudder'd upon the Bed;
At length with a feeble cry he said:

"When God commanded this hand to write
"In the studious hours of deep midnight,
"He told me the writing I wrote should prove
"The Bane of all that on Earth I lov'd.

"My Brother starv'd between two Walls,
"His Children's Cry my Soul appalls;
"I mock'd at the wrack & griding chain,
"My bent body mocks their torturing pain.

"Thy Father drew his sword in the North,
"With his thousands strong he marched forth;
"Thy Brother has arm'd himself in Steel
"To avenge the wrongs thy Children feel.

"But vain the Sword & vain the Bow,
"They never can work War's overthrow.
"The Hermit's Prayer & the Widow's tear
"Alone can free the World from fear.

"For a Tear is an Intellectual Thing,
"And a Sigh is the Sword of an Angel King,
"And the bitter groan of the Martyr's woe
"Is an Arrow from the Almightie's Bow.

"The hand of Vengeance found the Bed
"To which the Purple Tyrant fled;
"The iron hand crush'd the Tyrant's head
"And became a Tyrant in his stead."

WILLIAM BOND

I wonder whether the Girls are mad,
And I wonder whether they mean to kill,
And I wonder if William Bond will die,
For assuredly he is very ill.

He went to Church in a May morning
Attended by Fairies, one, two & three;
But the Angels of Providence drove them away,
And he return'd home in Misery.

He went not out to the Field nor Fold,
He went not out to the Village nor Town,
But he came home in a black, black cloud,
And took to his Bed & there lay down.

And an Angel of Providence at his Feet,
And an Angel of Providence at his Head,
And in the midst a Black, Black Cloud,
And in the midst the Sick Man on his Bed.

And on his Right hand was Mary Green,
And on his Left hand was his Sister Jane,
And their tears fell thro' the black, black Cloud
To drive away the sick man's pain.

"O William, if thou dost another Love,
"Dost another Love better than poor Mary,
"Go & take that other to be thy Wife,
"And Mary Green shall her servant be."

"Yes, Mary, I do another Love,
"Another I Love far better than thee,
"And Another I will have for my Wife;
"Then what have I to do with thee?

"For thou art Melancholy Pale,
"And on thy Head is the cold Moon's shine,
"But she is ruddy & bright as day,
"And the sun beams dazzle from her eyne."

When Mary woke & found her Laid
On the Right hand of her William dear,
On the Right hand of his loved Bed,
And saw her William Bond so near,

Mary trembled & Mary chill'd
And Mary fell down on the right hand floor,
That William Bond & his Sister Jane
Scarce could recover Mary more.

The Fairies that fled from William Bond
Danced around her Shining Head;
They danced over the Pillow white,
And the Angels of Providence left the Bed.

I thought Love liv'd in the hot sun shine,
But O, he lives in the Moony light!
I thought to find Love in the heat of day,
But sweet Love is the Comforter of Night.

Seek Love in the Pity of others' Woe,
In the gentle relief of another's care,
In the darkness of night & the winter's snow,
In the naked & outcast, Seek Love there!

THE SMILE

There is a Smile of Love,
And there is a Smile of Deceit,
And there is a Smile of Smiles
In which these two Smiles meet.

And there is a Frown of Hate,
And there is a Frown of disdain,
And there is a Frown of Frowns
Which you strive to forget in vain,

For it sticks in the Heart's deep Core
And it sticks in the deep Back bone;
And no Smile that ever was smil'd,
But only one Smile alone,

That betwixt the Cradle & Grave
It only once Smil'd can be;
But, when it once is Smil'd,
There's an end to all Misery.

MARY

Sweet Mary, the first time she ever was there,
Came into the Ball room among the Fair;
The young Men & Maidens around her throng,
And these are the words upon every tongue:

"An Angel is here from the heavenly Climes,
"Or again does return the Golden times;
"Her eyes outshine every brilliant ray,
"She opens her lips—'tis the Month of May."

Mary moves in soft beauty & conscious delight
To augment with sweet smiles all the joys of the Night,
Nor once blushes to own to the rest of the Fair
That sweet Love & Beauty are worthy our care.

In the Morning the Villagers rose with delight
And repeated with pleasure the joys of the night,
And Mary arose among Friends to be free,
But no Friend from henceforward thou, Mary, shalt see.

Some said she was proud, some call'd her a whore,
And some, when she passed by, shut to the door;
A damp cold came o'er her, her blushes all fled;
Her lillies & roses are blighted & shed.

"O, why was I born with a different Face?
"Why was I not born like this Envious Race?
"Why did Heaven adorn me with bountiful hand,
"And then set me down in an envious Land?

"To be weak as a Lamb & smooth as a dove,
"And not to raise Envy, is call'd Christian Love;
"But if you raise Envy your Merit's to blame
"For planting such spite in the weak & the tame.

"I will humble my Beauty, I will not dress fine,
"I will keep from the Ball, & my Eyes shall not shine;
"And if any Girl's Lover forsakes her for me,
"I'll refuse him my hand & from Envy be free."

She went out in Morning attir'd plain & neat;
"Proud Mary's gone Mad," said the Child in the Street;
She went out in Morning in plain neat attire,
And came home in Evening bespatter'd with mire.

She trembled & wept, sitting on the Bed side;
She forgot it was Night, & she trembled & cried;
She forgot it was Night, she forgot it was Morn,
Her soft Memory imprinted with Faces of Scorn,

With Faces of Scorn & with Eyes of disdain
Like foul Fiends inhabiting Mary's mild Brain;
She remembers no Face like the Human Divine.
All Faces have Envy, sweet Mary, but thine;

And thine is a Face of sweet Love in despair,
And thine is a Face of mild sorrow & care,
And thine is a Face of wild terror & fear
That shall never be quiet till laid on its bier.

SOME PEOPLE ADMIRE THE WORK OF A FOOL

Some people admire the work of a Fool,
For it's sure to keep your judgment cool;
It does not reproach you with want of wit;
It is not like a lawyer serving a writ.

SINCE ALL THE RICHES OF THIS WORLD

Since all the Riches of this World
May be gifts from the Devil & Earthly Kings,
I should suspect that I worship'd the Devil
If I thank'd my God for Worldly things.

WHY WAS CUPID A BOY?

Why was Cupid a Boy
And why a boy was he?
He should have been a Girl
For ought that I can see.

For he shoots with his bow,
And the Girl shoots with her Eye,
And they both are merry & glad
And laugh when we do cry.

And to make Cupid a Boy
Was the Cupid Girl's mocking plan;
For a boy can't interpret the thing
Till he is become a man.

And then he's so pierc'd with cares
And wounded with arrowy smarts,
That the whole business of his life
Is to pick out the heads of the darts.

'Twas the Greeks' love of war
Turn'd Love into a Boy,
And Woman into a Statue of Stone—
And away fled every Joy.

CROMEK SPEAKS

I always take my judgment from a Fool
Because his judgment is so very Cool,
Not prejudic'd by feelings great or small.
Amiable state! he cannot feel at all.

YOU SAY THEIR PICTURES WELL PAINTED BE

. . . . .

You say their Pictures well Painted be,
And yet they are Blockheads you all agree.
Thank God, I never was sent to school
To be Flog'd into following the Style of a Fool.

The Errors of a Wise Man make your Rule
Rather than the Perfections of a Fool.

Great things are done when Men & Mountains meet;
This is not done by Jostling in the Street

THE CAVERNS OF THE GRAVE I'VE SEEN

The Caverns of the Grave I've seen,
And these I shew'd to England's Queen.
But now the Caves of Hell I view:
Who shall I dare to shew them to?
What mighty Soul in Beauty's form
Shall dauntless View the Infernal Storm?
Egremont's Countess can controll
The flames of Hell that round me roll.
If she refuse, I still go on
Till the Heavens & Earth are gone,
Still admir'd by Noble minds,
Follow'd by Envy on the winds,
Re-engrav'd Time after Time,
Ever in their youthful prime,
My designs unchang'd remain.
Time may rage but rage in vain.
Far above Time's troubled Fountains
On the Great Atlantic Mountains,
In my Golden House on high,
There they Shine Eternally.

DEDICATION OF THE ILLUSTRATIONS TO BLAIR'S GRAVE

To the Queen

The Door of Death is made of Gold,
That Mortal Eyes cannot behold;
But, when the Mortal Eyes are clos'd,
And cold and pale the Limbs repos'd,
The Soul awakes; and, wond'ring, sees
In her mild Hand the golden Keys:
The Grave is Heaven's golden Gate,
And rich and poor around it wait;
O Shepherdess of England's Fold,
Behold this Gate of Pearl and Gold!

To dedicate to England's Queen
The Visions that my Soul has seen,
And, by Her kind permission, bring
What I have borne on solemn Wing
From the vast regions of the Grave,
Before Her Throne my Wings I wave;
Bowing before my Sov'reign's Feet,
"The Grave produc'd these Blossoms sweet
"In mild repose from Earthly strife;
"The Blossoms of Eternal Life!"

I ROSE UP AT THE DAWN OF DAY—

I rose up at the dawn of day—
Get thee away! get thee away!
Pray'st thou for Riches? away! away!
This is the Throne of Mammon grey.

Said I, "this sure is very odd.
"I took it to be the Throne of God.
"For every Thing besides I have:
"It is only for Riches that I can crave.

"I have Mental Joy & Mental Health
"And Mental Friends & Mental wealth;
"I've a Wife I love & that loves me;
"I've all but Riches Bodily.

"I am in God's presence night & day,
"And he never turns his face away.
"The accuser of sins by my side does stand
"And he holds my money bag in his hand.

"For my worldly things God makes him pay,
"And he'd pay for more if to him I would pray:
"And so you may do the worst you can do:
"Be assur'd Mr devil I won't pray to you.

"Then If for Riches I must not Pray,
"God knows I little of Prayers need say.
"So as a Church is known by its Steeple,
"If I pray it must be for other People.

"He says, if I do not worship him for a God,
"I shall eat coarser food & go worse shod;
"So as I don't value such things as these,
"You must do, Mr devil, just as God please."

From THE EVERLASTING GOSPEL

The Vision of Christ that thou dost see
Is my Vision's Greatest Enemy:
Thine has a great hook nose like thine,
Mine has a snub nose like to mine:
Thine is the friend of All Mankind,
Mine speaks in parables to the Blind:
Thine loves the same world that mine hates,
Thy Heaven doors are my Hell Gates.
Socrates taught what Meletus
Loath'd as a Nation's Bitterest Curse,
And Caiphas was in his own Mind
A benefactor to Mankind:
Both read the Bible day & night,
But thou read'st black where I read white.

. . . . .

God wants not Man to Humble himself:
This is the trick of the ancient Elf.
This is the Race that Jesus ran:
Humble to God, Haughty to Man,
Cursing the Rulers before the People
Even to the temple's highest Steeple;
And when he humbled himself to God,
Then descended the cruel Rod.
"If thou humblest thyself, thou humblest me;
"Thou also dwell'st in Eternity.
"Thou art a Man, God is no more,
"Thy own humanity learn to adore,
"For that is my Spirit of Life.
"Awake, arise to Spiritual Strife"

. . . . .

Humility is only doubt,
And does the Sun & Moon blot out,
Rooting over with thorns & stems
The buried Soul & all its Gems.
This Life's dim Windows of the Soul
Distorts the Heavens from Pole to Pole
And leads you to Believe a Lie
When you see with, not thro', the Eye
That was born in a night to perish in a night,
When the Soul slept in the beams of Light.

THE CRYSTAL CABINET

The Maiden caught me in the Wild,
Where I was dancing merrily;
She put me into her Cabinet
And Lock'd me up with a golden Key.

This Cabinet is form'd of Gold
And Pearl & Crystal shining bright,
And within it opens into a World
And a little lovely Moony Night.

Another England there I saw,
Another London with its Tower,
Another Thames & other Hills,
And another pleasant Surrey Bower,

Another Maiden like herself,
Translucent, lovely, shining clear,
Threefold each in the other clos'd—
O, what a pleasant trembling fear!

O, what a smile! a threefold Smile
Fill'd me, that like a flame I burn'd;
I bent to Kiss the lovely Maid,
And found a Threefold Kiss return'd.

I strove to sieze the inmost Form
With ardor fierce & hands of flame,
But burst the Crystal Cabinet,
And like a Weeping Babe became—

A weeping Babe upon the wild,
And Weeping Woman pale reclin'd,
And in the outward air again
I fill'd with woes the passing Wind.

I GIVE YOU THE END OF A GOLDEN STRING

I give you the end of a golden string:
Only wind it into a ball,
It will lead you in at Heaven's Gate
Built in Jerusalem's wall.

PART FOUR

From the Prophetic Books

From THE MARRIAGE OF HEAVEN AND HELL

. . . . .

Without Contraries is no progression. Attraction and Repulsion, Reason and Energy, Love and Hate, are necessary to Human existence.

From these contraries spring what the religious call Good & Evil. Good is the passive that obeys Reason. Evil is the active springing from Energy.

Good is Heaven. Evil is Hell.

. . . .

A Memorable Fancy

As I was walking among the fires of hell, delighted with the enjoyments of Genius, which to Angels look like torment and insanity, I collected some of their Proverbs; thinking that as the sayings used in a nation mark its character, so the Proverbs of Hell show the nature of Infernal wisdom better than any description of buildings or garments.

When I came home: on the abyss of the five senses, where a flat sided steep frowns over the present world, I saw a mighty Devil folded in black clouds, hovering on the sides of the rock: with corroding fires he wrote the following sentence now percieved by the minds of men, & read by them on earth:

How do you know but ev'ry Bird that cuts the airy way,
Is an immense world of delight, clos'd by your senses five?

Proverbs of Hell

In seed time learn, in harvest teach, in winter enjoy.
The road of excess leads to the palace of wisdom.
Prudence is a rich, ugly old maid courted by Incapcity.
Dip him in the river who loves water.
A fool sees not the same tree that a wise man sees.
He whose face gives no light, shall never become a star.
The busy bee has no time for sorrow.
The hours of folly are measur'd by the clock; but of wisdom,
no clock can measure.
All wholesome food is caught without a net or a trap.
Bring out number, weight & measure in a year of dearth.
No bird soars too high, if he soars with his own wings.
The most sublime act is to set another before you.
If the fool would persist in his folly he would become wise.
Folly is the cloke of knavery.
Shame is Pride's cloke.
Excess of sorrow laughs. Excess of joy weeps.
The fox condemns the trap, not himself.
Joys impregnate. Sorrows bring forth.
The bird a nest, the spider a web, man friendship.
What is now proved was once only imagin'd.
The cistern contains: the fountain overflows.

One thought fills immensity.
Every thing possible to be believ'd is an image of truth.
The eagle never lost so much time as when he submitted to learn of the crow.
Think in the morning. Act in the noon. Eat in the evening. Sleep in the night.
As the plow follows words, so God rewards prayers.
You never know what is enough unless you know what is more than enough.
The weak in courage is strong in cunning.
The apple tree never asks the beech how he shall grow; nor the lion, the horse, how he shall take his prey.
If others had not been foolish, we should be so.
The soul of sweet delight can never be defil'd.
When thou seest an Eagle, thou seest a portion of Genius; lift up thy head!
To create a little flower is the labour of ages.
Damn braces. Bless relaxes.
The crow wish'd every thing was black, the owl that every thing was white.
Exuberance is Beauty.
Improvement makes strait roads; but the crooked roads without Improvement are roads of Genius.
Where man is not, nature is barren.
Truth can never be told so as to be understood, and not be believ'd.
Enough! or Too much.

Selection from THE BOOK OF THEL

Thel's Motto

Does the Eagle know what is in the pit?
Or wilt thou go ask the Mole?
Can Wisdom be put in a silver rod?
Or Love in a golden bowl?

I

The daughters of the Seraphim led round their sunny flocks,
All but the youngest: she in paleness sought the secret air,
To fade away like morning beauty from her mortal day:
Down by the river of Adona her soft voice is heard,
And thus her gentle lamentation falls like morning dew:

"O life of this our spring! why fades the lotus of the water,
"Why fade these children of the spring, born but to smile & fall?
"Ah! Thel is like a wat'ry bow, and like a parting cloud;
"Like a reflection in a glass; like shadows in the water;
"Like dreams of infants, like a smile upon an infant's face;
"Like the dove's voice; like transient day; like music in the air.
"Ah! gentle may I lay me down, and gentle rest my head,
"And gentle sleep the sleep of death, and gentle hear the voice
"Of him that walketh in the garden in the evening time."

The Lilly of the valley, breathing in the humble grass,
Answer'd the lovely maid and said: "I am a wat'ry weed,
"And I am very small and love to dwell in lowly vales;
"So weak, the gilded butterfly scarce perches on my head.
"Yet I am visited from heaven, and he that smiles on all
"Walks in the valley and each morn over me spreads his hand,
"Saying, 'Rejoice, thou humble grass, thou new-born lilly
flower,
" 'Thou gentle maid of silent valleys and of modest brooks;
" 'For thou shalt be clothed in light, and fed with morning
manna,
" 'Till summer's heat melts thee beside the fountains and the
springs
" 'To flourish in eternal vales.' Then why should Thel com-
plain?
"Why should the mistress of the vales of Har utter a sigh?"

She ceas'd & smil'd in tears, then sat down in her silver shrine.

. . . . .

From AMERICA

A Prophecy

The Guardian Prince of Albion burns in his nightly tent:
Sullen fires across the Atlantic glow to America's shore,
Piercing the souls of warlike men who rise in silent night.
Washington, Franklin, Paine & Warren, Gates, Hancock &
Green
Meet on the coast glowing with blood from Albion's fiery
Prince.

Washington spoke: "Friends of America! look over the
Atlantic sea;
"A bended bow is lifted in heaven, & a heavy iron chain
"Descends, link by link, from Albion's cliffs across the sea,
to bind
"Brothers & sons of America till our faces pale and yellow,
"Heads deprest, voices weak, eyes downcast, hands work-
bruis'd,
"Feet bleeding on the sultry sands, and the furrows of the
whip
"Descend to generations that in future times forget."

The strong voice ceas'd, for a terrible blast swept over the
heaving sea:
The eastern cloud rent: on his cliffs stood Albion's wrathful
Prince,
A dragon form, clashing his scales: at midnight he arose,
And flam'd red meteors round the land of Albion beneath;
His voice, his locks, his awful shoulders, and his glowing
eyes
Appear to the Americans upon the cloudy night.

Solemn heave the Atlantic waves between the gloomy nations,
Swelling, belching from its deeps red clouds & raging fires.
Albion is sick! America faints! enrag'd the Zenith grew.
As human blood shooting its veins all round the orbed heaven,
Red rose the clouds from the Atlantic in vast wheels of blood,
And in the red clouds rose a Wonder o'er the Atlantic sea,
Intense! naked! a Human fire, fierce glowing, as the wedge
Of iron heated in the furnace: his terrible limbs were fire
With myriads of cloudy terrors, banners dark & towers
Surrounded: heat but not light went thro' the murky atmos-
phere.

The King of England looking westward trembles at the vision.

Albion's Angel stood beside the Stone of night, and saw
The terror like a comet

. . . . .

a voice came forth, and shook the temple:

"The morning comes, the night decays, the watchmen leave
their stations;
"The grave is burst, the spices shed, the linen wrapped up;
"The bones of death, the cov'ring clay, the sinews shrunk
& dry'd
"Reviving shake, inspiring move, breathing, awakening,
"Spring like redeemed captives when their bonds & bars are
burst.
"Let the slave grinding at the mill run out into the field,
"Let him look up into the heavens & laugh in the bright air;
"Let the inchained soul, shut up in darkness and in sighing,
"Whose face has never seen a smile in thirty weary years,
"Rise and look out; his chains are loose, his dungeon doors
are open;
"And let his wife and children return from the oppressor's
scourge.

"They look behind at every step & believe it is a dream,
"Singing: The Sun has left his blackness & has found a fresher
morning,
" 'And the fair Moon rejoices in the clear & cloudless night;
" 'For Empire is no more, and now the Lion & Wolf shall
cease.' "

. . . . .

"They cannot smite the wheat, nor quench the fatness of the
earth;
"They cannot smite with sorrows, nor subdue the plow and
spade;

"They cannot wall the city, nor moat round the castle of
princes;
"They cannot bring the stubbed oak to overgrow the hills;
"For terrible men stand on the shores, & in their robes I see
"Children take shelter from the lightnings: there stands
Washington
"And Paine and Warren with their foreheads rear'd toward
the east.
"But clouds obscure my aged sight. A vision from afar!
"Sound! sound! my loud war-trumpets, & alarm my thirteen
Angels! . . ."

. . . . .

Thus wept the Angel voice, & as he wept, the terrible blasts
Of trumpets blew a loud alarm across the Atlantic deep.
No trumpets answer; no reply of clarions or of fifes:
Silent the Colonies remain and refuse the loud alarm.

On those vast shady hills between America & Albion's shore,
Now barr'd out by the Atlantic sea, call'd Atlantean hills,
Because from their bright summits you may pass to the Golden
world,
An ancient palace, archetype of mighty Emperies,
Rears its immortal pinnacles, built in the forest of God
By Ariston, the king of beauty, for his stolen bride.

Here on their magic seats the thirteen Angels sat perturb'd,
For clouds from the Atlantic hover o'er the solemn roof.

Fiery the Angels rose, & as they rose deep thunder roll'd
Around their shores, indignant burning with the fires of Orc;
And Boston's Angel cried aloud as they flew thro' the dark
night.

He cried: "Why trembles honesty, and like a murderer
"Why seeks he refuge from the frowns of his immortal station?
"Must the generous tremble & leave his joy to the idle, to
the pestilence,
"That mock him? who commanded this? what God? what
Angel?

. . . . .

In the flames stood & view'd the armies drawn out in the sky,
Washington, Franklin, Paine, & Warren, Allen, Gates, &
Lee,
And heard the voice of Albion's Angel give the thunderous
command;
His plagues, obedient to his voice, flew forth out of their
clouds,
Falling upon America, as a storm to cut them off,
As a blight cuts the tender corn when it begins to appear.

. . . . .

The citizens of New York close their books & lock their
chests;
The mariners of Boston drop their anchors and unlade;
The scribe of Pennsylvania casts his pen upon the earth;
The builder of Virginia throws his hammer down in fear.

Then had America been lost, o'erwhelm'd by the Atlantic,
And Earth had lost another portion of the infinite,
But all rush together in the night in wrath and raging fire.

. . . . .

Albion's Guardian writhed in torment on the eastern sky,
Pale, quiv'ring toward the brain his glimmering eyes, teeth
chattering,
Howling & shuddering, his legs quivering, convuls'd each
muscle & sinew:
Sick'ning lay London's Guardian, and the ancient miterd York,
Their heads on snowy hills, their ensigns sick'ning in the sky.
The plagues creep on the burning winds driven by flames of
Orc,
And by the fierce Americans rushing together in the night,

. . . . .

Stiff shudderings shook the heav'nly thrones! France, Spain,
& Italy
In terror view'd the bands of Albion, and the ancient Guard-
ians,
Fainting upon the elements, smitten with their own plagues.
They slow advance to shut the five gates of their law-built
heaven,
Filled with blasting fancies and with mildews of despair,
With fierce disease and lust, unable to stem the fires of Orc.
But the five gates were consum'd, & their bolts and hinges
melted;
And the fierce flames burnt round the heavens & round the
abodes of men.

From THE FOUR ZOAS THE TORMENTS OF LOVE & JEALOUSY IN THE DEATH AND JUDGEMENT OF ALBION THE ANCIENT MAN

Vala

[Introduction to Night the First]

The Song of the Aged Mother which shook the heavens with wrath,
Hearing the march of long resounding, strong heroic Verse
Marshall'd in order for the day of Intellectual Battle.
The heavens quake, the earth was moved & shudder'd, & the mountains
With all their woods, the streams & valleys wail'd in dismal fear.

Four Mighty Ones are in every Man; a Perfect Unity
Cannot Exist but from the Universal Brotherhood of Eden,
The Universal Man, To Whom be Glory Evermore. Amen.
What are the Natures of those Living Creatures the Heav'nly Father only
Knoweth. No Individual knoweth, nor can know in all Eternity.

From Night the Second

[Enion's Complaint]

. . . . .

"I am made to sow the thistle for wheat, the nettle for a nourishing dainty.
"I have planted a false oath in the earth; it has brought forth a poison tree.
"I have chosen the serpent for a councellor, & the dog
"For a schoolmaster to my children.
"I have blotted out from light & living the dove & nightingale,
"And I have caused the earth worm to beg from door to door.

"I have taught the thief a secret path into the house of the just.
"I have taught pale artifice to spread his nets upon the morning.
"My heavens are brass, my earth is iron, my moon a clod of clay,
"My sun a pestilence burning at noon & a vapour of death in night.

"What is the price of Experience? do men buy it for a song?
"Or wisdom for a dance in the street? No, it is bought with the price

"Of all that a man hath, his house, his wife, his children.
"Wisdom is sold in the desolate market where none come to buy,
"And in the wither'd field where the farmer plows for bread in vain.

"It is an easy thing to triumph in the summer's sun
"And in the vintage & to sing on the waggon loaded with corn.
"It is an easy thing to talk of patience to the afflicted,
"To speak the laws of prudence to the houseless wanderer,
"To listen to the hungry raven's cry in wintry season
"When the red blood is fill'd with wine & with the marrow of lambs.

"It is an easy thing to laugh at wrathful elements,
"To hear the dog howl at the wintry door, the ox in the slaughter house moan;
"To see a god on every wind & a blessing on every blast;
"To hear sounds of love in the thunder storm that destroys our enemies' house;
"To rejoice in the blight that covers his field, & the sickness that cuts off his children,
"While our olive & vine sing & laugh round our door, & our children bring fruits & flowers.

"Then the groan & the dolor are quite forgotten, & the slave grinding at the mill,

"And the captive in chains, & the poor in the prison, & the soldier in the field
"When the shatter'd bone hath laid him groaning among the happier dead.

"It is an easy thing to rejoice in the tents of prosperity:
"Thus could I sing & thus rejoice: but it is not so with me."

From MILTON

A Poem in Two Books

And did those feet in ancient time
Walk upon England's mountains green?
And was the holy Lamb of God
On England's pleasant pastures seen?

And did the Countenance Divine
Shine forth upon our clouded hills?
And was Jerusalem builded here
Among these dark Satanic Mills?

Bring me my Bow of burning gold:
Bring me my Arrows of desire:
Bring me my Spear: O clouds unfold!
Bring me my Chariot of fire.

I will not cease from Mental Fight,
Nor shall my Sword sleep in my hand
Till we have built Jerusalem
In England's green & pleasant Land.

[Milton Rose Up]

Then Milton rose up from the heavens of Albion ardorous.
The whole Assembly wept prophetic, seeing in Milton's face
And in his lineaments divide the shades of Death & Ultro:
He took off the robe of the promise & ungirded himself from
the oath of God.

And Milton said: "I go to Eternal Death! The Nations still
Follow after the detestable Gods of Priam, in pomp
Of warlike selfhood contradicting and blaspheming.
When will the Resurrection come to deliver the sleeping body
From corruptibility?

. . . . .

And Milton said: "I go to Eternal Death!" Eternity shudder'd,
For he took the outside course among the graves of the dead,
A mournful shade. Eternity shudder'd at the image of eternal
death.

[The Nature of Infinity]

The nature of infinity is this: That every thing has its
Own Vortex, and when once a traveller thro' Eternity
Has pass'd that Vortex, he percieves it roll backward behind
His path, into a globe itself infolding like a sun,
Or like a moon, or like a universe of starry majesty,
While he keeps onwards in his wondrous journey on the earth,
Or like a human form, a friend with whom he liv'd benevolent.
As the eye of man views both the east & west encompassing
Its vortex, and the north & south with all their starry host,
Also the rising sun & setting moon he views surrounding
His corn-fields and his valleys of five hundred acres square,
Thus is the earth one infinite plane, and not as apparent
To the weak traveller confin'd beneath the moony shade. . . .

First Milton saw Albion upon the Rock of Ages,
Deadly pale outstretch'd and snowy cold, storm cover'd,
A Giant form of perfect beauty outstretch'd on the rock
In solemn death

. . . . .

[Open Your Human Gates]

Now Albion's sleeping Humanity began to turn upon his
Couch,
Feeling the electric flame of Milton's awful precipitate descent.
Seest thou the little winged fly, smaller than a grain of sand?

It has a heart like thee, a brain open to heaven & hell,
Withinside wondrous & expansive: its gates are not clos'd:
I hope thine are not: hence it clothes itself in rich array:
Hence thou art cloth'd with human beauty, O thou mortal
man.
Seek not thy heavenly father then beyond the skies,

. . . . .

[The Prophet]

"I am that Shadowy Prophet who Six Thousand Years ago
"Fell from my station in the Eternal bosom. Six Thousand
Years
"Are finish'd. I return! both Time & Space obey my will.
"I in Six Thousand Years walk up and down; for not one
Moment
"Of Time is lost, nor one Event of Space unpermanent,
"But all remain: every fabric of Six Thousand Years
"Remains permanent, tho' on the Earth where Satan
"Fell and was cut off, all things vanish & are seen no more,"

. . . . .

[O Go Not Forth in Martyrdoms & Wars!]

. . . . .

"O Sons, we live not by wrath, by mercy alone we live!
"I recollect an old Prophecy in Eden recorded in gold and oft

"Sung to the harp, That Milton of the land of Albion
"Should up ascend forward from Felpham's Vale & break the
Chain
"Of Jealousy from all its roots; be patient therefore, O my
Sons!

. . . . .

"Remember how Calvin and Luther in fury premature
"Sow'd War and stern division between Papists & Protestants.
"Let it not be so now! O go not forth in Martyrdoms & Wars!
"We were plac'd here by the Universal Brotherhood & Mercy
"With powers fitted to circumscribe this dark Satanic death . . .
"But how this is as yet we know not, and we cannot know
"Till Albion is arisen; then patient wait a little while.

. . . . .

"This thing
"Was never known, that one of the holy dead should willing
return.
"Then patient wait a little while till the Last Vintage is
over. . . ."

[The Four Faces of Man]

These are the starry voids of night & the depths & caverns
of earth.
These Mills are oceans, clouds & waters ungovernable in their
fury:
Here are the stars created & the seeds of all things planted,

And here the Sun & Moon recieve their fixed destinations.

But in Eternity the Four Arts, Poetry, Painting, Music
And Architecture, which is Science, are the Four Faces of
Man.
Not so in Time & Space: there Three are shut out, and only
Science remains thro' Mercy, & by means of Science the Three
Become apparent in Time & Space in the Three Professions,
That Man may live upon Earth till the time of his awaking.

[The Building of Time]

But others of the Sons of Los build Moments & Minutes &
Hours
And Days & Months & Years & Ages & Periods, wondrous
buildings;
And every Moment has a Couch of gold for soft repose,
(A Moment equals a pulsation of the artery),

. . . . .

And every Minute has an azure Tent with silken Veils:
And every Hour has a bright golden Gate carved with skill:
And every Day & Night has Walls of brass & Gates of
adamant,
Shining like precious Stones & ornamented with appropriate
signs:
And every Month a silver paved Terrace builded high:
And every Year invulnerable Barriers with high Towers:

And every Age is Moated deep with Bridges of silver & gold:
And every Seven Ages is Incircled with a Flaming Fire.
Now Seven Ages is amounting to Two Hundred Years.

. . . . .

For in this Period the Poet's Work is Done, and all the Great
Events of Time start forth & are conceiv'd in such a Period,
Within a Moment, a Pulsation of the Artery.

The Sky is an immortal Tent built by the Sons of Los:
And every Space that a Man views around his dwelling-place
Standing on his own roof or in his garden on a mount
Of twenty-five cubits in height, such space is his Universe:
And on its verge the Sun rises & sets, the Clouds bow
To meet the flat Earth & the Sea in such an order'd Space:

. . . . .

[The Choir of Day]

Thou hearest the Nightingale begin the Song of Spring.
The Lark sitting upon his earthy bed, just as the morn
Appears, listens silent; then springing from the waving Corn-
field, loud
He leads the Choir of Day: trill, trill, trill, trill,
Mounting upon the wings of light into the Great Expanse,
Reecchoing against the lovely blue & shining heavenly Shell,
His little throat labours with inspiration; every feather
On throat & breast & wings vibrates with the effluence Divine.

All Nature listens silent to him, & the awful Sun
Stands still upon the Mountain looking on this little Bird
With eyes of soft humility & wonder, love & awe,
Then loud from their green covert all the Birds begin their
Song:
The Thrush, the Linnet & the Goldfinch, Robin & the Wren
Awake the Sun from his sweet reverie upon the Mountain.
The Nightingale again assays his song, & thro' the day
And thro' the night warbles luxuriant, every Bird of Song
Attending his loud harmony with admiration & love.

. . . . .

[Bathe in the Waters of Life]

But turning toward Ololon in terrible majesty Milton
Replied: "Obey thou the Words of the Inspired Man.
"All that can be annihilated must be annihilated
"That the Children of Jerusalem may be saved from slavery.

. . . . .

"This is a false Body, in Incrustation over my Immortal
"Spirit, a Selfhood which must be put off & annihilated alway.

. . . . .

"To cast aside from Poetry all that is not Inspiration,
"That it no longer shall dare to mock with the aspersion of
Madness
"Cast on the Inspired by the tame high finisher of paltry Blots
"Indefinite, or paltry Rhymes, or paltry Harmonies,

"Who creeps into State Government like a catterpiller to
destroy;
"To cast off the idiot Questioner who is always questioning
"But never capable of answering, who sits with a sly grin
"Silent plotting when to question, like a thief in a cave,
"Who publishes doubt & calls it knowledge, whose Science
Is Despair,
"Whose pretence to knowledge is Envy, whose whole Science
is
"To destroy the wisdom of ages to gratify ravenous Envy
"That rages round him like a Wolf day & night without rest:"

. . . . .

[The Last Vision]

And I beheld the Twenty-four Cities of Albion
Arise upon their Thrones to Judge the Nations of the Earth;
And the Immortal Four in whom the Twenty-four appear
Fourfold

. . . . .

Applied their Four Trumpets & them sounded to the Four
winds.

Terror struck in the Vale I stood at that immortal sound.
My bones trembled, I fell outstretch'd upon the path
A moment, & my Soul return'd into its mortal state
To Resurrection & Judgment in the Vegetable Body,

And my sweet Shadow of Delight stood trembling by my side.

Immediately the Lark mounted with a loud trill from Felpham's
Vale,
And the Wild Thyme from Wimbleton's green & impurpled
Hills,

. . . . .

Their Wine-presses & Barns stand open, the Ovens are pre-
par'd,
The Waggons ready; terrific Lions & Tygers sport & play.
All Animals upon the Earth are prepar'd in all their strength
To go forth to the Great Harvest & Vintage of the Nations.

From JERUSALEM THE EMANATION OF THE GIANT ALBION

[*Blake's Task*]

Trembling I sit day and night, my friends are astonish'd at
me,
Yet they forgive my wanderings. I rest not from my great
task!
To open the Eternal Worlds, to open the immortal Eyes
Of Man inwards into the Worlds of Thought, into Eternity
Ever expanding in the Bosom of God, the Human Imagination.
O Saviour pour upon me thy Spirit of meekness & love!
Annihilate the Selfhood in me: be thou all my life!
Guide thou my hand, which trembles exceedingly upon the
rock of ages,
While I write. . . .

[*England! Awake!*]

England! awake! awake! awake!
Jerusalem thy Sister calls!
Why wilt thou sleep the sleep of death
And close her from thy ancient walls?

Thy hills & valleys felt her feet
  Gently upon their bosoms move:
Thy gates beheld sweet Zion's ways:
  Then was a time of joy and love.

And now the time returns again:
  Our souls exult, & London's towers
Recieve the Lamb of God to dwell
  In England's green & pleasant bowers.

[The Fields from Islington to Marybone]

  The fields from Islington to Marybone,
To Primrose Hill and Saint John's Wood,
  Were builded over with pillars of gold,
And there Jerusalem's pillars stood.

. . . . .

  Her Little-ones ran on the fields,
The Lamb of God among them seen,
  And fair Jerusalem his Bride,
Among the little meadows green.

  Pancrass & Kentish-town repose
Among her golden pillars high,
  Among her golden arches which
Shine upon the starry sky.

. . . .

She walks upon our meadows green,
The Lamb of God walks by her side,
And every English Child is seen
Children of Jesus & his Bride.

. . . . .

Jerusalem fell from Lambeth's Vale
Down thro' Poplar & Old Bow,
Thro' Malden & across the Sea,
In War & howling, death & woe.

The Rhine was red with human blood,
The Danube roll'd a purple tide,
On the Euphrates Satan stood,
And over Asia stretch'd his pride.

. . . . .

The Divine Vision still was seen,
Still was the Human Form Divine,
Weeping in weak & mortal clay,
O Jesus, still the Form was thine.

And thine the Human Face, & thine
The Human Hands & Feet & Breath,
Entering thro' the Gates of Birth
And passing thro' the Gates of Death.

And O thou Lamb of God, whom I
Slew in my dark self-righteous pride,
Art thou return'd to Albion's Land?
And is Jerusalem thy Bride?

Come to my arms & never more
Depart, but dwell for ever here:
Create my Spirit to thy Love:
Subdue my Spectre to thy Fear.

. . . . .

A man's worst enemies are those
Of his own house & family;
And he who makes his law a curse,
By his own law shall surely die.

In my Exchanges every Land
Shall walk, & mine in every Land,
Mutual shall build Jerusalem,
Both heart in heart & hand in hand.

[It Is Easier to Forgive an Enemy]

"It is easier to forgive an Enemy than to forgive a Friend.
"The man who permits you to injure him deserves your vengeance:
"He also will recieve it; go Spectre! obey my most secret desire
"Which thou knowest without my speaking. Go to these Fiends of Righteousness,
"Tell them to obey their Humanities & not pretend Holiness
"When they are murderers: as far as my Hammer & Anvil permit.
"Go, tell them that the Worship of God is honouring his gifts
"In other men: & loving the greatest men best, each according
"To his Genius: which is the Holy Ghost in Man; there is no other
"God than that God who is the intellectual fountain of Humanity.

. . . . .

"I have tried to make friends by corporeal gifts but have only
"Made enemies. I never made friends but by spiritual gifts,
"By severe contentions of friendship & the burning fire of thought.
"He who would see the Divinity must see him in his Children,"

. . . . .

Albion reply'd: "Cannot Man exist without Mysterious

"Offering of Self for Another? is this Friendship & Brotherhood?
"I see thee in the likeness & similitude of Los my Friend."

Jesus said: "Wouldest thou love one who never died
"For thee, or ever die for one who had not died for thee?
"And if God dieth not for Man & giveth not himself
"Eternally for Man, Man could not exist; for Man is Love
"As God is Love; every kindness to another is a little Death
"In the Divine Image, nor can Man exist but by Brotherhood."

So saying the Cloud overshadowing divided them asunder.
Albion stood in terror, not for himself but for his Friend
Divine; & Self was lost in the contemplation of faith
And wonder at the Divine Mercy & at Los's sublime honour.

"Do I sleep amidst danger to Friends? O my Cities & Counties,
"Do you sleep? rouze up, rouze up! Eternal Death is abroad!"

. . . . .

"Awake, Awake, Jerusalem! O lovely Emanation of Albion,
"Awake and overspread all Nations as in Ancient Time;
"For lo! the Night of Death is past and the Eternal Day
"Appears upon our Hills. Awake, Jerusalem, and come away!"

. . . . .

INDEXES

Index of Titles

Index of First Lines

ABOUT THE COMPILER

Throughout her long career as librarian and teacher of librarians, Amelia Munson has devoted herself to work with young adults, and her especial enthusiasm has been for poetry. In addition to her work in The New York Public Library, Miss Munson has written a book, *An Ample Field,* addressed to library workers with young people, compiled a reading list of "Poetry for High Schools," which has been adopted for use in colleges as well, and for many years taught graduate courses in adolescent reading and appreciation at the Columbia School of Library Science.

She has done a great deal of speaking, before groups of all ages, and she says that "no matter what the topic, poetry has always managed to get in."

Miss Munson lives in New York City. Her interests, besides reading, include "music—as an auditor, sports—as a spectator, and theater—as it used to be."

EVANSTON TOWNSHIP HS
EVANSTON, IL 60204
101 112123